West India South Dock, London, and Number 1 warehouse, about 1875. The massive multi-storey warehouse was typical of the kind of secure, long-term storage building erected to serve nineteenth-century sailing ship docks in many ports. On the knuckle of the quay are a capstan and capstan bars used for ship handling within the docks.

OLD DOCKS

Nancy Ritchie-Noakes

Shire Publications Ltd

CONTENTS

Harbours, ports and docks 3
The development of dock
  systems in Britain 1700-1900 6
Dock construction 19
Dock operation: cargo handling
  and water regime 23
Redundancy, closure and
  redevelopment 31
Further reading 32
Places to visit 32

Set in 9 point Times roman and printed in Great Britain by C. I. Thomas & Sons (Haverfordwest) Ltd, Press Buildings, Merlins Bridge, Haverfordwest, Dyfed.

British Library Cataloguing in Publication Data available.

COVER: *View in 1984 across Canning Half-tide Basin (1844) to the north stack of warehouses, Albert Dock (1845) in Liverpool. The basin was designed to function as a large lock giving access to several docks otherwise cut off from the river Mersey. In 1984 the river entrance was fitted with new flap gates so that the basin could continue to serve its original purpose, albeit for historic vessels and pleasure craft only. The warehouses on the north side of Albert Dock now form part of Merseyside Maritime Museum.*

BELOW: *Repairs to the walls, Town Quay, Southampton, in the 1920s. In the background (from left) are nineteenth-century warehouses and the remains of the fifteenth-century water gate to the medieval town, all of which still stand.*

The White Star liner 'Teutonic', sister ship of the ill-fated 'Titanic', in the newly completed Alexandra Graving Dock, Belfast, 1889. Because there was no shortage of land in the port and new docks did not have to be built on the sites of old ones, Belfast possesses a unique sequence of graving docks dating from the late eighteenth century to the middle of the twentieth.

HARBOURS, PORTS AND DOCKS

Harbours are coastal places of shelter for ships; they may or may not be provided with ancillary facilities for ship and cargo handling. Ports are coastal or inland towns or cities possessing harbours to which vessels resort at the beginning or end of voyages and for loading and unloading. A port can exist without any addition to the natural shelter it affords to shipping, but over the centuries the exigencies of trade have made the viability of this kind of primitive port impossible. Archaeological investigations along the London waterfront have revealed that the Romans constructed massive timber quays and associated buildings from the middle of the first century AD, and in subsequent centuries timber piers and breakwaters were erected in many parts of the outports. It was not until the eighteenth century that docks were built in British ports, and thereafter, though a dock system was neither an essential nor a unique feature of any port, it constituted its most important appendage.

Wet docks are areas of impounded water within which vessels can remain afloat at a uniform level, independent of external tidal action. Dry docks are those from which water can be temporarily excluded in order that repairs and maintenance to hulls or keels of vessels can be effected. When a vessel is floated into a dock and the water is then removed by natural or artificial means, the appropriate term is a *graving dock*. Passage to and from wet and graving docks is through gates which open, depending on

ABOVE: *View of the inside of a graving dock, port of Liverpool. When the underwater body of a ship requires repair, examination or cleaning, the vessel is floated into a dry dock, where it settles on to keel blocks along the centre of the dock as the water is pumped out. Dry docks in shipyards are also used for building and fitting out.*

BELOW: *The 'Asia' and the Littlehampton-registered barge 'Moultonian' tied up at the north quay, Inner Dock, Southampton, about 1900. 'E' Warehouse on the right is all that remains of this dock.*

4

Belfast Harbour Office, 1985. Since the early nineteenth century the grand designs and important settings of custom houses and dock company and port authority headquarters have reflected the standing of their builders in the maritime commercial community. The Belfast Harbour Office was built in three sections to designs by the Board's engineers George Smith (1854), W. H. Lynn (1895) and Hobart and Heron (1970). Smith's section incorporated a clock tower (the top of which is visible here between the two right-hand chimneys) to regulate the punctual sailing of passenger steamers.

the local tidal range and the general sophistication of the dock system, direct to the harbour waters or to another dock or to a lock similar to a canal lock. A locked entrance permits vessels to enter it at any time when there is enough water to allow them to clear the outer sill; the water level in the dock is not affected and access to the dock is not restricted to the few hours around high water. Locks between docks in the same system make it possible to maintain different water levels in adjacent basins if required.

Though the subject of this book is old docks, a port does not comprise docks alone. A typical port may include addi-tionally a pilotage authority and a conservancy authority (responsible for maintaining approach channels, dredging, surveying the tideway, preventing pollution, lighting and buoying, removing wrecks and so on), a dock labour board, customs and immigration authorities, a port health authority and port police. There may also be numerous private and public wharfingers, lighterage and towage firms, master stevedores and master porters, shipping companies, brokers and forwarding agents and inland transport undertakings, all of whose requirements may impinge on the design and operation of particular dock systems.

5

Quantities of timber floating in Norway Dock (built about 1812) in the Surrey Docks, London, about 1875. Cargoes of timber were not warehoused, and in the nineteenth century large balks of unsawn timber were stored in the docks before being loaded on to barges or towed to sawmills. The change to importing much more sawn timber and the demand for better use of dock room both contributed to the discontinuance of this practice.

THE DEVELOPMENT OF DOCK SYSTEMS IN BRITAIN 1700-1900

The reasons why docks were needed in general and why they were built in particular locations in particular ports help to explain the early history of dock building in Britain. The first dock proper in Britain was the 10 acre (4 ha) Howland Great Wet Dock, which was built at Rotherhithe on the Thames between 1697 and 1700 as a safe place for light (that is empty) ships to lie up. The Howland Dock had no quays and no customs business was transacted there, because in common with other major ports at the time the problem to be solved by dock construction was not to facilitate cargo handling but to ease the congestion caused by a superabundance of light ships laid up for the winter or engaged on seasonal trades. It was said that in the haven at Hull ships lay several deep along

the quay and sometimes small ships became suspended between larger ones as the tide went out and the big ships grounded.

It was in the port of Liverpool in 1715 that the first commercial wet dock was opened. The Mersey has a tidal range of 30 feet (9 metres), the shoals and navigation channels shift constantly and the tide race is strong. Before the building of the docks, the height of the tide enabled ships of deep draught to reach the town quay and the slight shelter offered by the Pool, the tidal inlet to the south of the quay. But the only ships that could safely lie close to the town were those that could take the ground at low water; those which needed to float at all states of the tide had to anchor far out into the Mersey where they were exposed to the weather, to the

6

hazards of the river and to great difficulties in the discharge of cargoes. When hulls were short and stout and planking was thick and strong vessels could ground with impunity. Bigger and less sturdily constructed ships would suffer serious strain or even collapse under such drastic treatment.

Commercial docks were not built in London until the beginning of the nineteenth century, when congestion, caused by laden vessels (in 1791 ten thousand coasters and 3500 ocean-going vessels came up to London to vie with 3400 lighters for river room), and pilferage impelled two merchants' companies to begin dock and warehouse construction. Until then the Thames had provided sufficient space and safety to render docks unnecessary; the waterfront was lined with wharves and even today it is possible to see at low water the grids laid on the foreshore to give barges an even berth alongside.

Docks were built, too, in canal ports, at the seaward end of canals or where new cuts were made between the port and the sea. Such docks were intended to improve canal trade by assisting the locking of barges between canal and navigable river and the transfer of goods between barge and ship. The Grand Surrey Canal Company's basin, opened in 1807, was used extensively for shipping and eventually became part of the Surrey Commercial Docks. Between 1773 and 1800 three basins were built at Runcorn by the Duke of Bridgewater although his dock in Liverpool (Duke's Dock) became the place where the bulk of transhipment occurred. In 1793 a group of merchants in Gloucester obtained an Act of Parliament to enable them to build a canal between Gloucester and Berkeley Pill that would be large enough to admit ships of 400 tons burden; this would not only allow existing through traffic to avoid the treacherous parts of the upper Severn estuary but would also help to develop the port of Gloucester as a rival to Bristol. The basins at Gloucester eventually covered some 10 acres (4 ha) and were provided with an impressive range of warehouses.

Once the general need for an area of impounded water was identified, it was next necessary to settle on a construction site. Bird in *Major Seaports of the United Kingdom* summarises the four physical factors that decide the location of a port, and, by extension, of its docks: (1) the land site — the actual area of land

View of Queen's Dock, Glasgow (opened 1880), showing steam sailing ships about 1900. Notably absent from the port of Glasgow are the multi-storey warehouses which are a feature of the ports of London, Liverpool and Hull. Transit sheds were used instead because the port was the rapid-transit servicing centre for the Highlands and Islands.

Internal loading docks or barge holes (typical of canal company architecture) at Duke's Dock grain warehouse, Liverpool, 1958. The warehouse was built in 1811 and demolished in 1960 when the barge docks were filled in.

installations and their immediate physical surroundings; (2) the land situation — the position with relation to the physical geography of the hinterland the port serves; (3) the water site — the harbour; (4) the water situation — the nature of the water approaches from the nearest sea lanes. The impact of various of these factors on dock development, when considered along with non-physical factors such as sources of finance, ownership of land and influence of vested interests, is manifested in the histories of individual British ports.

The most important of the early dock systems were built at Liverpool and Hull in the eighteenth century and London and Bristol in the early nineteenth century. Liverpool's first dock was built in the mouth of the Pool, a site which was suitable both for its relative ease of development and for its proximity to the commercial centre of the borough. Powers to raise the money for dock construction and to collect dues levied on ships using the port were given by Act of Parliament to the council of the borough as trustees. The site was easier to develop physically because it was not out in the river, and it was easier to develop politically because the Pool did not belong to private owners with interests to be

ABOVE: *Goole docks around 1910 with the parish church and the remarkable coal hoist designed by W. H. Bartholomew and constructed in 1864 by Armstrong's. Goole docks were developed by the Aire and Calder Navigation according to a John Rennie design carried out by the company's engineer, George Leather, in the 1820s. The estate comprised ship and barge docks connected by a collecting basin, warehouses, sheds, offices, a custom house and a patent slip for the repair of 300-400 ton vessels.*

BELOW: *The lower basin in the canal port docks at Ellesmere Port, about 1910, with narrow boats and dumb barges in the dock. Part of the warehouse designed by Telford and built in 1829 is visible on the right; on the left are flour mills and in the centre warehouses for clay and grain. Part of the overhead crane on the iron ore wharf can also be seen on the left.*

bought out. Though Liverpool claimed at this time to be the third largest port in the kingdom, it was a relatively new port, with the consequential advantage for dock building that the commercial centre such as it was could be reorganised to fit in with dock construction and operation. A succession of town halls and custom houses was built ever closer to 'Old Dock' and by the mid eighteenth century these municipal buildings as well as many of the glassworks, saltworks and sugar refineries which consumed Liverpool's imports were clustered about the dock.

Liverpool's first dock was the only one to be built on an inland site in that port; all of the rest were constructed along the waterfront, on sites reclaimed from the foreshore. The reasons for this were topographical: on the landward side was a high ridge of sandstone, overlain only in places by boulder clay and unsuitable for excavations, and on the estuarine side the shore shelved too steeply for dock construction by river reclamation to be a possibility. At Birkenhead, on the other side of the Mersey, the topography was ideal for dock building, but the geography was wrong because Liverpool was the centre of commerce and population.

Although Liverpool's second dock engineer, Henry Berry, was engaged to build the first dock at Hull from 1774, there were two significant differences between the provision of docks in the two places. First, Hull adopted inland not waterfront sites. To dissuade local merchants from promoting a dock for light ships outside the established trading area, the Crown offered a central site free: the land covered by the ancient fortifications still surrounding the town. Secondly, the Hull dock was built by private enterprise. Initial negotiations for the enabling Act of Parliament had been between the council and the Board of Customs and then, as Jackson has put it, with no ceremony and no recorded reason, those principally involved in the negotiations suddenly deviated from this well-trodden path and produced the Hull Dock Company, the first dock company in Britain.

The SS 'Gypsy' aground at Horseshoe Bend in the river Avon in 1878 with the Bristol tug 'Sea King' (built 1875) attending. The tortuous and dangerous river passage to Bristol City Docks was a great impediment to shipping, and many of those who tried to save the cost of a tug had to pay the price of their ships in the end.

10

The rear of warehouses on the north side of Import Dock, West India Docks, London, about 1920. Built early in the nineteenth century, all but two stacks at the west end of the dock were destroyed by bombing in 1940.

Also built by a private company was Bristol Floating Harbour, a 70 acre (28 ha) dock designed by William Jessop in 1803 and opened in 1809. It was made by cutting a new channel from the Avon to the south of the city and then impounding part of the old channel which ran through the town. The existing river quays continued to be used. A precedent for the Floating Harbour had been built at Grimsby and opened in 1800, but since Grimsby had then nothing to offer but her 15 acre (6 ha) dock the plan to divert trade from Hull came to nought and provided typical evidence that docks and ports are not mutually inclusive.

Commercial dock building began relatively late in London, largely because for a long time the Thames served so well as an anchorage. Nevertheless, by the mid eighteenth century merchants had begun to petition for the extension of the legal quays which, together with the additional 'sufferance wharves', were the only places where goods could be legally landed in the presence of the collector of Royal Customs or under specific licence. The situation became unbearable as a result of significant increases in trade, much of it seasonal, which created traffic jams on the river. Eventually the West India Dock Act (1799) and the London Dock Act (1800) were obtained to enable the two merchants' companies to build docks which were to have their own legal quays and bonded warehouses, towering perimeter walls and private police forces. The site for the West India Docks was the Isle of Dogs, then a boggy waste used only for the grazing of cattle. In general the location was suitable because Limehouse, Greenwich and Blackwall Reaches had been the common eighteenth-century anchorages for large ocean-going vessels, and in particular the acreage required for the 30 acre (12 ha) Import Dock, the 24 acre (10 ha) Export Dock, the two entrance basins and the

The steam locomotive 'Bristol' on the dockside at Avonmouth docks, about 1950.

ABOVE: *Roadway and sidings at the rear of Harrington Dock transit sheds, Liverpool, and an overhead crane for lifts of up to 10 tons.*

BELOW: *'Queen Mary' and 'Homeric' among the vessels in Ocean Dock, Southampton, June 1955. Also visible are Floating Crane Number 1, a troopship, 'Southern Cross', in Trafalgar Dry Dock and a flying boat at the BOAC post-war terminal. In the top left corner are the town quay and Royal Pier with Western Docks in the distance.*

warehouses, cartways and 12 foot (4 metre) wide thief-deterring ditch was too great to be easily accommodated in a built-up area. Distance from the City and its warehouses was not a problem, partly because of the provision of massive stacks of bonded warehouses at West India Docks and partly because of improved land transport links such as the Commercial Road built as a joint venture between the two dock companies. The City Canal (opened 1805) was built at the City's expense across the Isle of Dogs to cut off the inconvenient U bend in the river round by Greenwich.

The London Docks were built on a site in Wapping and though the principal dock (Western Dock) was only 20 acres (8 ha) in size, some 1300 houses had to be demolished between 1800 and 1805 to make room for this first phase of construction. More than half of the total expenditure to 1806 was due to the purchase of property, and it was many years before the whole scheme could be finished. The East India Company's ships had traditionally anchored at Blackwall and the East India Docks were opened there in 1806, exclusively for company vessels, partly on the site of the shipbuilder John Perry's 1790 fitting-out Brunswick Dock. Unlike the West India and London Docks, these docks had no warehouses attached: the company's valuable imports continued to be carried by road under escort to its City warehouse stronghold in Cutler Street. Bulky, relatively low-value cargoes such as timber needed much larger dock estates than those required for goods from the West and East Indies, and cheaper sites (less densely built up and populated) were developed on the other side of the river by various companies from around 1804.

The first phase of dock construction in the port of London culminated in the opening in 1828 of St Katharine's Dock on a narrow site (comprising 1033 houses

Royal Victoria Dock, London, originally constructed in 1850-5, extensively rebuilt in 1935-44 and remodelled in the late 1950s. The layout of the dock as shown epitomises modern dock operation; import cargoes are discharged from ship to shed for sorting, packaging and customs purposes and then transferred to railway wagons or lorries for inland distribution; export cargoes are delivered by road or rail to the docks from where they are loaded into outward-bound coastal or ocean-going vessels.

An aerial view of King George Dock, Hull, opened in 1914, with the exceptionally narrow entrance lock visible on the left side of the picture. This 'joint dock' was built by the North Eastern and Hull and Barnsley Railways (including Hull Dock Company, which had sold out to the NER in 1893). It was designed to cater for coal and grain as well as general trade, which accounts for its unusual shape.

and the medieval church and hospital of St Katharine by the Tower) between the Tower and London Docks. The development was promoted by a company which had been formed to take advantage of the free trade movement which began when Parliament did not renew the East India Company's monopoly over Indian trade. The chosen site, later adjudged to be 'ridiculously small and ruinously expensive', was intended to enable the dock to benefit from proximity to the City. However, when St Katharine's was still under construction the first steam train was running and the massive warehouse which surrounded the new basins were unsuitable for the working of the new steamships; the grandiose St Katharine's Dock was outmoded from the outset.

From the 1830s onwards throughout the rest of the nineteenth century, old docks were rebuilt and new ports with new docks were developed all over Britain — not only because of expanding trade but also because of new trades and new ships and cargo-handling machinery. The coming of the railways required docks to be built or rebuilt with land carriage in mind. Steamers required more dock room than sailing ships and could not be crowded together (they wanted a quick turnaround) nor mixed with sailing vessels. Hydraulic and steam cargo-handling machinery accelerated loading and unloading. Larger and larger transoceanic passenger liners needed berths.

In Liverpool Clarence Dock (1830) was built for steamships on a site to the north of the central docks, in order to isolate the steamers, which were still thought to be a fire risk. The fitting of 70 foot (21 metres) gates to the Coburg Dock in 1840

ABOVE: *West Bute Basin, Cardiff, in the 1860s with sailing vessels awaiting the tide. The basin and dock were built in 1835-9 and closed in 1963.*

BELOW: *In the foreground are Eastern Docks, Southampton, in the early 1930s and the 1924 floating dock (for repairs to liners). In the middle ground are the Inner Dock (the port's only enclosed dock) and the Outer Dock; the Inner Dock was filled in 1965 and the Outer Dock was redeveloped for cross channel roll-on/roll-off traffic. In the background is the river Itchen, where wharves are still used for ship repair and the aggregate, gravel and scrap metal trades.*

ABOVE: *Roath Dock, Cardiff, crowded with tramp steamers about 1920. The early coal docks (West and East Bute) in Cardiff had soon become too small for modern ships and it was the building of the Roath Dock (opened 1887) and Queen's Dock (opened 1907) which was responsible for the port's prosperity up to 1913. Roath Dock remains in use.*

BELOW: *Southampton's Outer Dock in 1889 with entrances to dry docks Numbers 1, 2 and 3 in the foreground and Peninsular and Oriental's 'Arcadia' in the centre.*

transformed this dock into the only one in the port able to receive ocean-going paddle steamers. Two floating landing stages, together measuring over 1000 feet (305 metres) long, were built off Prince's Dock wall to accommodate passenger liners. Between 1821 and 1888 nearly thirty docks were built or rebuilt on the Liverpool side of the Mersey.

In Hull Railway Dock was opened in 1846 to bring the Hull and Selby Railway into the dock system; Victoria Dock was opened in 1850 for steamers. In London the Victoria Dock Company was formed to build some modern docks. The company was led by two great railway contractors, Peto and Brassey, and Victoria Dock (1855) was provided with extensive railway links, internal jetties to extend quay length, hydraulic cargo-handling machinery and transit sheds. The site of the enormous new 100 acre (40 ha) dock lay down river on the marshes where land was cheap and where large steamers would not be endangered by overcrowding in the narrow reaches. Another railway-linked dock was opened in 1868 by the Millwall Dock Company on the Isle of Dogs; as at Victoria Dock, the entrance lock was 80 feet (24 metres) wide, its dimensions crucial to the success of the dock it served.

The first of the new docks built by and for a railway company was the Victoria Dock in Hartlepool, opened in 1840 by the Hartlepool Dock and Railway Company; curiously, as the result of bitter competition for trade, in 1847 West Dock was opened in West Hartlepool by the Stockton and Hartlepool Railway Company a few hundred yards up the line from Victoria Dock. After fifteen years of planning, a large coal dock (Hudson Dock) was opened in Sunderland in 1850, whilst the building of a coal dock by local businessmen at Middlesbrough resulted in a 29 per cent increase in coal exports between 1841 and 1844. Docks such as these were built in new places because there was insufficient room on existing dock estates to meet the railway companies' land requirements.

Northumberland Dock (1857) at Newcastle, Marshall Dock (1859) at Silloth, Cumbria, and docks at Workington (1865), Maryport (1867 and 1884), Whitehaven (1876) and Barrow-in-Furness (1867) were built for the coal, iron ore and iron and steel trades. The building of the West Bute Dock (1839) enabled Cardiff to become the main coal port in South Wales, and though docks were opened at Newport (1842) and Swansea (1852) these did not rival Cardiff's, whose position was consolidated by the construction of East Bute Dock in 1855. Railway docks were built for general trade at Grimsby and Birkenhead around the middle of the nineteenth century. In the early days Grimsby was a great success; Birkenhead was not: the port had nothing to offer a hinterland already served by Liverpool and the development company ran out of money before the bulk of their scheme could be realised.

One of several types of port which could operate successfully in modern times without docks was the packet port, used by the boats which primarily carried mail and passengers. These trades needed neither access to deep water nor extensive cargo-handling facilities, and places such as Dover, Newhaven, Harwich, Holyhead and Portpatrick could provide adequate accommodation simply by building piers and breakwaters. Southampton was in a different position because transatlantic (as against cross-channel) steamers did need deep water; the Southampton Dock Company was formed in 1840 and by 1851 the port had two docks.

From the last quarter of the nineteenth century until the beginning of the First World War, economic and operational changes took place which required the reconstruction or change of use of established dock systems and these changes were manifested in the way the late nineteenth- and early twentieth-century docks were built and run.

Dock reconstruction in the port of Liverpool, 1908. Note the 'hollow wall' construction top left.

DOCK CONSTRUCTION

The forerunners of commercial wet docks in Britain were locks and docks made by utilising the natural flow of water in rivers and harbours. Beaumaris Castle (begun in 1295) on the isle of Anglesey included a controlled supply of tidal water for the moat and a dock into which a fully laden 40 ton ship could sail right up to the castle wall at high tide. The pound lock, whereby a body of water was held up by a dam, originated on the continent of Europe in the fifteenth century and was introduced to contain and deepen rivers in England in the sixteenth century, for instance on the Exeter Canal (about 1564). At Deptford on the south bank of the Thames a naval dockyard was established during the reign of Henry VII (1485-1509) for the building and repair of the king's ships, and a dock was built there around 1542, some two years after the construction of a similar dock at Portsmouth dockyard. The dockyard docks consisted of dry docks, basically docks from which water was excluded after it had flowed out naturally or pound locks in reverse, and some small wet docks for fitting out. The immediate precursor of the first commercial dock (in Liverpool) was the Howland Great Wet Dock, a fitting-out dock for the merchant marine. As the first Liverpool dock was built in the mouth of the Pool it represented no significant technological advance over its ancestors. Its walls were made of brick set in ordinary lime mortar and backed with rubble. Structurally, this first dock was not much of a success: periodically parts of the walls collapsed due to natural causes and neighbouring shipbuilders made matters worse by tearing down other sections in order to launch their ships into the dock.

Dock walls will fail unless they can withstand their own weight on their foundations, the pressure of water within the dock and the pressure of the backing behind the walls (especially when the docks were drained for cleaning or repair). Walls can overturn, settle, slide and fracture unless erected on sound foundations and tied adequately into the material of the backing, but the means to these ends were beyond the contemporary knowledge and experience of the early dock engineers. Further, it was not until the 1750s when Smeaton brought from the Netherlands the discovery of 'tarras mortar' for his Eddystone Lighthouse that a water-resistant binding agent was available to the dockbuilders. By the end of the eighteenth century, however, much had been learned from earlier failures, some new technology was available and a number of outstanding engineers had begun to specialise in docks and harbour work.

After a debacle at Grimsby sea lock when the mud walls of the dock collapsed, the stone walls of the lock sank and the wooden floor of the lock was blown up by the pressure of the underlying mud, John Rennie was called in to design a scheme which could be used in harbours with poor foundations. He built an enormous timber raft, anchored by piles, protected at both ends by sheet piling and resting on an inverted brick arch and he floated the lock on this structure. Though a structure of this complexity was not needed in Liverpool for the early docks which hugged the foreshore and which were founded on rock, docks built out into the Mersey many years later were constructed according to Rennie's general ideas. Rennie also introduced at Grimsby the idea of building 'hollow' walls, that is, walls built with arched recesses in them to reduce their weight. This practice too was followed subsequently in much nineteenth-century dock construction.

Another notable engineer of the time was William Jessop, who was responsible

Fairbairn steam crane, 1876, built by Stothert and Pitt of Bath for Bristol City Docks. This unique survivor is now in the care of Bristol City Museums.

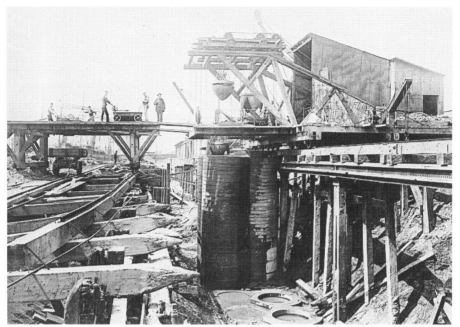

Clyde Trustees' own works at Riverside Quay, June 1878. Where the nature of the ground (running sand, artesian water, soft heaving clay or silt for instance) makes it undesirable to lay the foundation walls in open trenches, an alternative is to sink cylinders into the difficult ground and fill them with concrete so that they act as a sort of piling. On this foundation the dock wall is built. The cylinders here are made up of a pile of concrete rings on top of which are loaded cast iron rings of the same diameter to force the cylinders down as the excavation of sand from within the cylinders proceeds.

for the Bristol Floating Harbour, docks in Dublin and the West India Docks and City Canal in London. Ralph Walker was consulting engineer to the East India Docks. Thomas Telford was appointed as engineer to St Katharine's Dock and to the Ellesmere and Chester Canal Company, which built docks at Ellesmere Port.

Steam engines had been in use for some time for pumping out mines, and an obvious extension of their application was to the drainage of dock excavations. Rennie had been the first to use steam power for purposes other than pumping, at the Albion Mills he built for Boulton and Watt, and he was probably the first to use a steam engine for pile driving, at London Docks in 1802. Steam was used to drive mortar mills and to haul some railway wagons, but digging was done by spadework and spoil was carried out of the excavations in barrows. The men who built the docks were sometimes employed directly by the dock company or port authority and sometimes by independent contractors who had tendered successfully for particular parts of the whole job. Similarly, the engineers worked sometimes as employees, sometimes as consultants. Transport of materials to and from the sites was at first on wooden and later on iron railways, in wagons drawn by horses in the early days and eventually by locomotives.

Throughout the nineteenth century expertise grew, more machinery was used and the people who did the design and construction work were increasingly likely to be an organised team of consulting engineers and specialist contractors. Steam navvies replaced muscle power. In 1875 electric light was first used on a dock contract (Albert Dock, London), enabling work to continue after dark. Brick and stone were replaced by concrete, and timber (for piles and gates) by iron and steel.

21

A common adjunct to dock construction, primarily in the nineteenth century, was the building of warehouses. The basic functional requirements of warehouses were robust construction (so as not to collapse when filled with tons of rice and sugar), flexibility of internal spaces (to accommodate various cargoes), security (protection from weather, theft and fire) and systems for moving goods into, out of and around the buildings. Most warehouses were built of brick, made where possible using clay from the dock excavations, and many were embellished with stone quoins, parapets and other decorative features. Until the mid nineteenth century the internal construction of dock warehouses remained of timber, even though iron-framed town warehouses and textile mills had been built in Britain since the 1790s. The Albert Warehouses in Liverpool were the first dockside warehouses to be built entirely of incombustible materials — brick, stone and iron, including an iron roof on iron trusses. Although the British engineer Ralph Dodd had taken out a patent in 1808 for including wrought iron bars in concrete, it was not until the very end of the nineteenth century that modern reinforced concrete construction was introduced to Britain by Francois Hennebique. This technique was particularly suitable for warehouses because of its great strength and fire resistance. Other advances in concrete construction technology included the use of pre-cast piles and rafts on difficult ground.

Albert Dock, Liverpool, built in the early 1840s, was used until around 1890 as a discharging dock for deep-sea sailing ships from the Far East, India and the Americas and made redundant by the ascendancy of large steamers.

Barrels of wine in store at Avonmouth docks about 1895.

DOCK OPERATION: CARGO HANDLING AND WATER REGIME

The primary function of a commercial dock system is cargo handling so commercial dock design should take account of cargo types and packages and the requirements of the carriers, distributors and administrators who deal with the cargoes. Consequently, what is on the ground in dockland will generally reflect contemporary economic and technical developments in shipping and commerce. In the early days of dock construction cargo handling was less important than ship safety and facilities for handling goods were rudimentary or non-existent. Using manual tackle, ships' hands and/or local dockers discharged cargoes on to quaysides open to thieves and rain. Each consignee had to find his own goods and have them removed by carters to warehouses in the town. In an age when voyage times were somewhat erratic and merchants made money not only from importing and exporting but also from acting as brokers, agents, bankers, underwriters and shipowners, efficiency on the quayside was not paramount.

By the end of the eighteenth century the move to build warehouses as integral parts of the new docks was evidence of change. These warehouses gave merchants the twin advantages of security and efficiency. Additionally, under an Act of 1803, importers were permitted to land goods without payment of duty (until delivered for domestic consumption) provided they gave some security for the duties and the goods were deposited in secure warehouses. Cargo handling itself was still laborious. Every bale (silk), bag (cotton), barrel (rum), puncheon (palm oil), cask (ginger), frail (figs), firkin (tallow), hogshead (tobacco), bullock, pig and the occasional harpsichord had to be manhandled from ship

23

ABOVE: *A cargo of bananas en route from ship to ripening warehouse by conveyor belt, Avonmouth docks, about 1920. Orginally the bananas were carried all the way by hand.*

BELOW: *The 'Union Castle' mail boat at 102 Berth in the Western Docks, Southampton, which were built in the early 1930s. The transit sheds are post-war. In the background are Rank's Solent Flour Mills and the sidings and carriage cleaning sheds for six full boat trains.*

A railway carriage for the South Indian Railway being exported from the port of Liverpool in the 1920s.

to quay to shed to warehouse or to lighter and vice versa. The warehouses were provided with a variety of manual hoists and treadmill cranes worked by gangs of men relieving each other in succession so as to keep the apparatus in continuous operation. Yardarm rigs, winches and shipboard derricks were available too, but muscle power was still the most significant mover of tons of cargo. Goods bound to and from the docks by road were carried by horse power and wagons created the same congestion on the quaysides and highways as ships created in the tideways.

In 1846 William Armstrong built the first hydraulic dockside crane and installed it at Newcastle Quay; in 1847 the Liverpool dock engineer Jesse Hartley ordered two lifts and two cranes for the newly completed Albert Warehouses. This was the first application of hydraulic power to port operations in Britain. Within ten years all existing docks north of the Thames in London had adopted hydraulic power for some purposes, and hydraulic pumping stations were a feature of nearly all of the major ports.

Hydraulic machinery was immensely valuable because it was powerful, speedy and flexible and eminently practical because it could be supplied wherever a pipe could be laid. It was particularly important in the coaling ports and in the coaling docks of the general ports where railway wagons full of coal could be raised to any height and their contents tipped into ships' holds. Nevertheless, hydraulic power was neither as extensively nor as quickly adopted as might have been expected, and this was because it was still cheaper in some cases to employ manual labour than to invest in an hydraulic installation. The strategy of declining to modernise infrastructure and machinery because it was cheaper in the short term to use the available army of dock workers was one which plagued all ports to some degree right up to the 1970s and eventually contributed to the closure of the docks worst affected.

Until about 1865 when the compound marine engine was developed, giving more than twice as much mileage out of a ton of coal as previously, long deep-sea voyages for steamers were uneconomic.

Passengers, mail and some fine freight had been moving by steamer since the 1820s, but the coal bunkers on these ships took up so much space that little room was left for heavier cargo. The change-over from sail to steam affected dockside cargo handling in several ways. Iron-hulled steam freighters were expensive to build, and when they were not steaming between ports they were not earning money for their owners, who therefore wanted turnaround times to be as short as possible. Quick turnarounds were feasible: inland transport along an extensive railway network was fast and reliable; steamships' schedules were regular and relatively unaffected by the weather; steamers could use their own steam-driven gear to facilitate discharge and loading of cargoes. One consequence of all this speed and predictability was that huge multi-storey warehouses became redundant. Long-term storage was no longer necessary or desirable for most commodities. Warehouses such as those at Albert Dock, Liverpool, and St Katharine's Dock, London, were particularly useless because they were built hard on the quay edge and so provided almost no room for rapid unloading. The new requirement was for transit sheds, mostly single-storey, with numerous dockside openings and planned to accommodate rail links to the hinterland.

Throughout the nineteenth century buildings for particular cargoes had been built in many ports and they had been distinguished primarily by their structural or internal spatial characteristics. Tobacco warehouses, for instance, featured bay sizes determined by the dimensions of hogsheads. From the end of the century such famous milling firms as Pauls, Spillers, Ranks and McDougalls began to build waterside granaries and flour mills. Their lofty silos made these buildings structurally distinctive, while their pneumatic grain-handling plant and milling machinery distinguished them operationally from dockside buildings whose main function was temporary storage. The development of bulk handling of cargoes other than grain also affected the landscape of dockland, though the structures erected for cargoes of coal and fuel oil were not buildings at all. Bulk coal handling became practicable with the introduction of hydraulic hoists and reached its nineteenth-century apogee in the form of the unique barge hoists at Goole. Installations for bulk oil, built mostly from the early 1920s, comprised jetties (within an impounded dock at Swansea but elsewhere out in the river), pipelines and 'tank farms' (clusters of oil storage tanks on shore). After the Second World War cargoes such as sugar, sulphur (as a heated liquid) and wine began to be shipped in bulk. Traditional dockside sheds and warehouses were useless for bulk cargoes and indeed dockside buildings were not needed wherever pipelines could connect ships to, for example, bulk sugar stores or vatting establishments.

The amount of water available in a harbour and the timing of its availability are facts of geography. The particular skill of the harbour engineer lies in designing a scheme, subject to technical limitations, which exploits or circumvents local conditions as necessary. Where there is no great tidal range, open docks (for example, Glasgow) are satisfactory provided there is an adequate depth of water over the dock sill. In ports where the difference between high and low waters is great (for example, Liverpool) dock gates are vital. Furthermore, in such ports locked entrances with gates at each end are needed if ships are to be able to enter the docks during longer periods than the two hours on either side of high tide. Until the mid nineteenth century the size of lock gates was limited severely by the difficulty of working them manually. Thereafter the perfection of Armstrong's hydraulic machinery and its application to gate operation made it possible to install gates whose size reflected the dimensions of contemporary modern ships.

Since every gate marks a place in a dock system where water has to be crossed, pedestrian and road bridges have been a common feature of dock estates from earliest times. Though none of the huge eighteenth-century timber drawbridges survives, numerous examples of other types remain from the nineteenth and early twentieth centuries: cast iron and steel, swing and bascule,

ABOVE: *Coaling the SS 'Yearby' at a 25 ton steam crane on the north quay, Queen's Dock, Glasgow, 14th July 1878.*
BELOW: *Toxteth Dock, Liverpool, about 1890. The Liverpool dock engineer G. F. Lyster patented these travelling hydraulic roof cranes, which were manufactured by Armstrong, Mitchell. The cranes were designed to work in tandem with ships' gear, with the cranes discharging into the upper storey and the ships' gear filling the quay level of the transit sheds.*

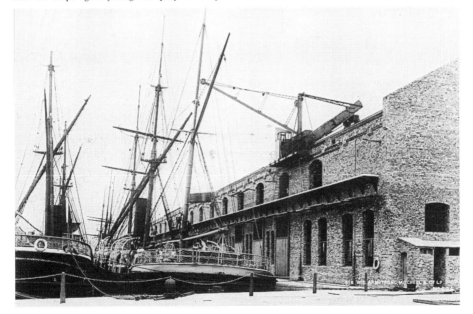

ABOVE: *Engine houses (left), boiler house (centre) and hydraulic pressure centre and accumulator tower (right) and residences (over engine houses and hpc), Langton Graving Docks, Liverpool, designed by G. F. Lyster and built in 1879. The complex was built to pump out the graving docks and to provide hydraulic power for the machinery at the graving docks. The hpc and accumulator tower have been demolished.*

BELOW: *The tug 'Defiance' in the lock pit of Alexandra Dock, Hull, in the 1880s. The swingbridge across the lock was hydraulically operated.*

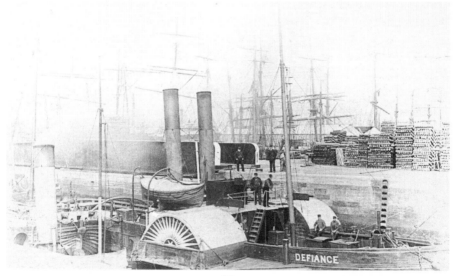

ABOVE: *The SS 'Caronia' alongside Number 32 shed, Tilbury Dock, London, in the 1920s, with Babcock and Wilcox quayside cranes. Goods unloaded into Thames lighters were delivered to specialised warehousing in another dock or on the riverside, to another ship or to canal or riverside industrial premises such as granaries. Most lighters were towed by tugs, but work over short distances could be undertaken by 'driving' the lighters with the use of oars 26 feet (8 metres) long.*

BELOW: *Loading bales of wool on to railway wagons at the rear of triple-storey transit sheds in Liverpool's north docks in the 1920s.*

manual and hydraulic, and railway bridges. A few pedestrian bridges also remain, although pedestrians often had to make do with a handrail installed across the tops of the gate leaves.

Another physical factor limiting access to docks is silt. Dredging is thus of critical importance in port management. Before mechanical dredgers were available, accumulated mud in docks was removed by men wielding shovels and by sluicing, using water let out of adjoining docks. Mechanical dredgers fitted with an end-less chain of buckets were brought into use in the late eighteenth century, and credit for building the first steam dredger is variously given to John Rennie or Richard Trevithick. Suction dredgers were developed later for use on very fine silt and soft mud. Where dredging, sometimes in combination with sluicing through wing walls, failed to ensure adequate depths of water economically or at all the affected docks and harbours were bound to be closed to shipping.

Iron ore being unloaded from a ship's hold in the 1950s at Rothesay Dock, Clydebank, which was designed specifically for the export of coal and the import of iron ore. The preponderance of dry cargo imports (including grain, sugar, timber, crude fertilisers and metal ores) is shipped in bulk.

Millwall Docks, London, under construction about 1869. Clearly visible are the chains by which the gate leaves were pulled open and the rollers and roller paths on which the leaves travelled when opening.

REDUNDANCY, CLOSURE AND REDEVELOPMENT

By the end of the 1960s even the most active of the major British ports contained large areas of dockland which were no longer viable. Previously important trades such as coal and passengers had declined precipitously. Modern ships could not negotiate the narrow entrances and shallow sills of the old docks. Container and roll-on/roll-off traffic called for extensive areas of empty quay, furnished with giant straddle carriers or with ramps for stern loading and discharging. The location of markets had changed, and airports had taken trade away from the maritime ports. The port authorities had no choice but to close their docks to commercial shipping. The vast acreages of disused and then derelict land and water thus created posed considerable redevelopment problems, many of which have been successfully solved, in economic terms at least. A number of old docks

and warehouses have become museums whose collections and displays often include historic vessels. Art galleries, exhibition centres, marinas, shops, restaurants and garden festivals have begun to occupy places where once no one would have ventured for recreation. Some of the old docks have once more become places of work — but the work is rarely port work and the workers are not dockers. Where once the only residences on the docks were the 'tied' dwellings of dockmasters and other officials, millions of square feet of warehouses have been converted to desirable residences for the relatively rich. Finally, whilst the old working docks were places of restricted access, the redeveloped docks invite visitors, for whom much material evidence of the docks' varied histories remains to be seen.

FURTHER READING

Carr, R. J. M. (editor). *Dockland*. NELP/GLC, 1986.
Conway-Jones, H. *Gloucester Docks*. Alan Sutton, 1984.
Jackson, G. *The History and Archaeology of Ports*. World's Work Ltd, 1983. (An excellent introduction to port history in general, with useful bibliography and good illustrations.)
Lord, J., and Southam, J. *The Floating Harbour*. Redcliffe Press, 1983.
Porteous, J. D. *Canal Ports*. Academic Press, 1977.
Ritchie-Noakes, N. *Liverpool's Historic Waterfront*. HMSO, 1984.

Also worth consulting are the *Industrial Archaeology of ...* series published by David and Charles, and old technical books, *Minutes of the Proceedings of the Institute of Civil Engineers* and *Transactions of the Newcomen Society*, which can be found in major public libraries.

PLACES TO VISIT

Most docks are dangerous and not open to the public. The exceptions are the places which have been redeveloped for recreation and commerce. Some museums which are situated in docklands and/or display collections relating to docks are listed below. Intending visitors are advised to find out the opening times before making a special journey.

The Boat Museum, Dockyard Road, Ellesmere Port, Cheshire L65 4EF. Telephone: 051-355 5017.
Bristol Industrial Museum, Princes Wharf, Bristol, Avon BS1 4RN. Telephone: Bristol (0272) 299771.
Merseyside Maritime Museum, Pier Head, Liverpool L3 1DN. Telephone: 051-709 1551.
Museum in Docklands Visitor Centre, 'W' Warehouse, Royal Victoria Dock, North Woolwich, London E16. Telephone: 01-511 2612. (Visitors by appointment only.)
Southampton Maritime Museum, The Wool House, Bugle Street, Southampton, Hampshire. Telephone: Southampton (0703) 23941.
Town Docks Museum, Queen Victoria Square, Hull, North Humberside HU1 3DX. Telephone: Hull (0482) 222737.
Welsh Industrial and Maritime Museum, Bute Street, Cardiff, South Glamorgan CF1 6AN. Telephone: Cardiff (0222) 481919.

ACKNOWLEDGEMENTS
    The author thanks the people who supplied the illustrations and also those who gave particular help with her research, namely Robert Aspinall (Museum of London), Andy King (Bristol Industrial Museum), Reginald Norfolk, MBE and Nigel Overton (Southampton Maritime Museum). Photographs on the following pages are acknowledged to: Belfast Harbour Commissioners, page 5; the Boat Museum Trust, page 9 (lower); Bristol City Museum, pages 10, 20; City of Hull Museums (Town Docks Museum), pages 15, 28 (lower); Humberside City Council Leisure Services, page 9 (upper); Merseyside Maritime Museum, pages 4 (upper), 13 (upper), 19, 22, 25, 28 (upper), 29 (lower); Port of Bristol Authority, pages 12, 23, 24 (upper); Port of London Authority Collection, Museum in Docklands, pages 1, 6, 11, 14, 29 (upper), 31; Royal Commission on Historical Monuments (England), page 8; Southampton Maritime Museum, pages 2, 4 (lower), 13 (lower), 16 (lower), 17 (lower), 24 (lower); Strathclyde Regional Archives, pages 7, 21, 27 (both), 30; Ulster Museum, page 3; Welsh Industrial and Maritime Museum, Cardiff, pages 16 (upper), 17 (upper). The cover picture is by the author.